Ramshacl

Poems

Also available from Macmillan

The Apple-Raid
poems for Year 6
chosen by Pie Corbett

An Odd Kettle of Fish
poems by John Rice, Pie Corbett and Brian Moses

Read Me 2
A poem for every day of the year
chosen by Gaby Morgan

The Works
Every kind of poem you will ever need
for the Literacy Hour
chosen by Paul Cookson

Another Day On Your Foot And I Would Have Died
poems by John Agard, Wendy Cope, Roger McGough,
Adrian Mitchell and Brian Patten

Ramshackle Rainbow

Poems for Year 5

Chosen by Pie Corbett

MACMILLAN CHILDREN'S BOOKS

First published 2001
by Macmillan Children's Books
a division of Pan Macmillan Limited
20 New Wharf Road, London N1 9RR
Basingstoke and Oxford
www.panmacmillan.com

Associated companies throughout the world

ISBN 0 330 48290 4

1 3 5 7 9 8 6 4 2

A CIP catalogue record for this book is available from the British Library.

Printed by Mackays of Chatham plc, Chatham, Kent.

Contents

Introduction

An anthology can be like a family, or a gathering of old friends. I'd like you to meet some of mine. Many of these poems I have known for a long time. Coming back to them I realize that they are so strong that the passing of time seems to have enriched their meaning. But there are also some new additions – fresh sparks that caught my eye like sudden gleams of sunlight. Sharply cut diamonds that reflect some facet of who we are.

I suppose I am lucky – my poetry family is quite large. So, how was I to choose the 60 or so poems for this book? Well, in a way it was easy enough. At first hundreds of old friends jostled for attention. But I wanted poems that I had shared with children on many occasions. Poems that I knew would appeal, would interest and fascinate. Poems that would resonate in the mind long after their reading. So they had to be strong poems.

I wanted to bring together poems that were related – so that they would sometimes speak to each other in their own language, echoing back and forth across the pages. I wanted to have poems that I knew would not always be too easily grasped. Poems that might need thinking about. Not everything in life is easy to understand and sometimes the most mysterious are the most amazing – I could never fathom how a magnet works, but they have always fascinated me. Why don't rainbows wobble in the wind? Just because things are difficult to understand does not mean they cannot intrigue, or be beautiful. Poems are not like simple sums – these old friends cannot always be tied down easily, but meet them, greet them and enjoy them.

And I wanted poems that could act as a kick-start to writing. Many of these poems are old standbys – faithful retainers, who have helped thousands of children find poetry within themselves, a self-confidence to put a word in, their word. Many of these poems have been the catalyst to children's own writing – and I have been lucky enough to witness some remarkable poems being written, in moments when something of our common genius poked its nose round the corner to surprise us all. So, I needed poems that I knew could strengthen imagination, release invention and ignite writing. If you like, this collection is a toolbox for creative teachers, readers and writers.

Finally, I imagined myself with a class of Year 5 children and thought about what poetry equipment we might need to take us through the journey of a year together. Poems that we could lean upon, poems that would surprise us, poems of many shades and moods. Poems that did not patronize. Poems that might light up a lifetime.

Of course, I wanted the poems to reflect the national literacy strategy. So, there are poems by significant poets, longer classic poems, narrative poetry, poems from a variety of cultures as well as choral and performance poems. There are poems that echo different shades of meaning and patterns. Some use figurative language such as simile, metaphor and personification as well as poems that are multi-layered and challenging. Also there are concrete poems where the design is crucial. All this is included – but, to be honest, whilst this helped to sharpen the choice, it never hindered. And besides, I wanted poems so strong that they would speak to others – those interested in writing in secondary schools and beyond.

Not just poems written for a ten year old. But poems that had demanded to be written.

So, step inside – meet this gathering of old friends and relations. Give them some time and you will get to know them well – and, maybe, make friends for life. You may even be tempted to create a few – take a step out of the darkness of yourself. Step into sunlight. It feels good to make new friends, to create something new.

Pie Corbett
March 2001

From *Auguries of Innocence*

To see a World in a Grain of Sand
And a Heaven in a Wild Flower,
Hold Infinity in the palm of your hand
And Eternity in an hour.

William Blake

Secret

Tell me your secret.
I promise not to tell.
I'll guard it safely at the bottom of a well.

Tell me your secret.
Tell me, tell me, please.
I won't breathe a word, not even to the bees.

Tell me your secret.
It will be a pebble in my mouth.
Not even the sea can make me spit it out.

John Agard

Benediction

Thanks to the ear
that someone may hear

Thanks to seeing
that someone may see

Thanks to feeling
that someone may feel

Thanks to touch
that one may be touched

Thanks to flowering of white moon
and spreading shawl of black night
holding villages and cities together

James Berry

Les Etiquettes Jaunes

I picked up a leaf
today from the sidewalk
This seems childish.

Leaf! you are so big!
How can you change your
colour, then just fall!

As if there was no
such thing as integrity!

You are too relaxed
to answer me. I am too
frightened to insist.

Leaf! don't be neurotic
like the small chameleon.

Frank O'Hara

Clouds

In the clouds I saw –
an old man resting in a wooden bed,
a judge's head bowing angrily.
A resting pig snorting.
A dropping Daddy
bending over
a wishing mountain.
A sulking woman sobbing.
A dove angel perched
on a rainbow tree.
A rolling brick banging
on the solid ground,
a stretching balloon popping.
A lipstick lady
driving a kissing car.
An angry crocodile
sneezing.

Teddy Corbett

A poem to be spoken silently . . .

It was so silent that I heard
my thoughts rustle
like leaves in a paper bag . . .

It was so peaceful that I heard
the trees ease off
their coats of bark . . .

It was so still that I heard
the paving stones groan
as they muscled for space . . .

It was so silent that I heard
a page of this book
whisper to its neighbour,
"Look he's peering at us again . . ."

It was so still that I felt
a raindrop grin
as it tickled the window's pane . . .

It was so calm that I sensed
a smile crack the face
of a stranger . . .

It was so quiet that I heard
the morning earth roll over
in its sleep and doze
for five minutes more . . .

Pie Corbett

Rain

Like a drummer's brush,

the rain hushes the surfaces of tin porches.

Emanuel diPasquale

Before the Hunt

Howling wind,
  hear me,
Dancing trees,
  hail me,
Cooling breeze,
  calm me,
Guiding sky,
  light my
way through the bush.
  As the stars
protect the lonely moon
  So may I
escape the snares
  in this living forest
  As the cat
stalks its prey
So may I
Be first to spy my game
  Living forest, hear me,
Chilling wind, still my heart,
Teasing shadows, smile with
  me,
Lead me to my hunt.

Lari Williams
Nigeria

Winter Morning

Milk bottles chattering
Out on the step in the cold.

Icicles shattering,
Licked but too tricky to hold.

Children mad-hattering,
Late for school, slippery-soled.

Sue Cowling

Splinter

The voice of the last cricket

across the first frost

is one kind of goodbye.

It is so thin a splinter of singing.

Carl Sandburg

Winter

No teeth, no hands, but it still bites.

Snow

I flew like an eagle, fell like a king, died like a dog.

Vasko Popa

Sunday Morning Diary Poem

This Sunday morning
surprised by birdsong.
Sun warms roofs,
casts cool sharp shadows –

though the road glitters.
Frost gilds
each
step.

Daisy and Teddy
run on ahead,
their voices echo
up the narrow lane
to Sunday school.

A marmalade cat
sneaks by greystone walls,
a blackbird sets off an alarm,
calls an early warning . . .

Trees are still skeletal,
from stark patterns
against a blue sky.

After weeks of grey fog
and sudden snow –
it feels good
to know the sun's
kindly glow –

to catch birdsong
as it drifts along
the lanes.

Pie Corbett

Heatwave

Heat over all; a lark can rise
Into the arching sun;
The moor like a lion sleeping lies –
Rough mane on burning stone.
Not a harebell shakes; the wild blue flags
Of wind are folded up.
Here on the hill the air is still
As water in a cup.

Phoebe Hesketh

Summer Rain

Here it is so quiet
you can hear the twigs
whispering to each other.
Every leaf sags
under the heavy gold of the sun.
Such a wealth of gold
even the day stands still
holds its breath
to keep the gold from spilling
down into the weeds and underbrush

Georgi Djagarov
Bulgaria

Fog

The fog comes
on little cat feet.
It sits looking
over harbour and city
on silent haunches
and then moves on.

Carl Sandburg

Where Would You Be?

Where would you be on a night like this
With the wind so dark and howling?
Close to the light
Wrapped warm and tight
Or there where the cats are prowling?

Where would you wish you on such a night
When the twisting trees are tossed?
Safe in a chair
In the lamp-lit air
Or out where the moon is lost?

Where would you be when the white waves roar
On the tumbling storm-torn sea?
Tucked inside
Where it's calm and dry
Or searching for stars in the furious sky
Whipped by the whine of the gale's wild cry
Out in the night with me?

Karla Kuskin

The Sea

The sea is a hungry dog,
Giant and grey.
He rolls on the beach all day,
With his clashing teeth and shaggy jaws
Hour upon hour he gnaws
The rumbling, tumbling stones,
And 'Bones, bones, bones, bones!'
The giant sea-dog moans,
Licking his greasy paws.

And when the night wind roars
And the moon rocks in the stormy cloud,
He bounds to his feet and snuffs and sniffs,
Shaking his wet sides over the cliffs,
And howls and hollos long and loud.

But on quiet days in May and June,
When even the grasses on the dune
Play no more their reedy tune,
With his head between his paws
He lies on the sandy shores
So quiet, so quiet, he scarcely snores.

James Reeves

The Tide Rises, The Tide Falls

The tide rises, the tide falls.
The twilight darkens, the curlew calls;
Along the sea-sands damp and brown
The traveller hastens to the town,
And the tide rises, the tide falls.

Darkness settles on roofs and walls,
But the sea, the sea in the darkness calls;
The little waves with soft, white hands,
Efface the footprints in the sands,
And the tide rises, the tide falls.

The morning breaks; the steeds in their stalls
Stamp and neigh, as the hostler calls;
The day returns, but nevermore
Returns the traveller to the shore,
And the tide rises, the tide falls.

Henry Wadsworth Longfellow

Beach

Our territories
of towels
dissolve at the water's edge.
Brief comedies of
yell and scream,
push and pull,
splash and dive,
end in the sea's forgiving arms.
We emerge to
the applause of waves.

John Coldwell

Wind and Silver

Greatly shining,

The autumn moon floats in the thin sky;

And the fish-ponds shake their backs and

flash their dragon scales

As she passes over them.

Amy Lowell

This Morning I Have Risen Early

A cairn of cloud
on the mountain peak.
A curragh of cloud
on the black-blue sea.

This morning I have risen early.

A dawn-calling gull
on the scarlet seawind.
A wounded swan
and she in the scattering mist.

This morning I have risen early.

A grazing cow
on a jacket of green field.
A brindled calf
eating the buttercup buttons.

This morning I have risen early.

A razed house
as still as salt on its own grey shadow.
A rugged castle
cold as ashes in its skin of stone.

This morning I have risen early.

A spit of rock
drying black and saffron.
A thick-lipped seal
waking us with her gruff reef-songs.

Tomorrow I shall rise at daybreak.

John Rice

Atlantic Roundhouse

Under the mists
  the frost of salt.
Under the salt,
  the cushion thrift.
Under the thrift,
  the freckled stones.
Under the stones,
  the parent rock.
Under the rock,
  the foolish past.
Under the past,
  the precious anchor.

John Rice

Sunset

Horse chestnut leaves hang
waiting like wing-folded bats
for the day to die.

Trees on hilltops creep
like caterpillar suppers
into the sun's mouth.

Blossoms blush shyly
shamed by sly, frosty fingers
that nip at night-time.

Tarmac and tussocks
seep into shared grey slumber
through day's dulling eyes.

Clusters of glow-worms
shiver down in the valley
under dusk's thin sheet.

Over sleeping hills
a patchwork quilt of May greens
breathes for tomorrow.

Wind prays through grasses
as silent, white choirboys sway
at Today's funeral.

Gina Douthwaite

Coltsfoot

Coming before my birthday they are forever your
flowers

Who are dead and at whose hand

I picked them on the allotments and blitzed land.

David Constantine

Three Kings

Out of wintry shadows wind sped like an arrow
earth and water froze.
Albert wheeled his barrow,
leaning on his load. 'Christmas Day tomorrow.'
'On the downs it snowed,' cried George, 'it's coming
soon.'
Frank looked up the road.

That dark afternoon a stranger walked ahead
haloed by the moon.
He half turned: 'Peace,' he said.
Wind dropped.
Like a sign a star rose up,
and led that moment out of time,
as if his gentle call
made earth and heaven rhyme.

Like a miracle
George, Frank and Albert felt
drawn into his will.

Lamplight seemed to melt,
with a wild grace stars circled down
To pelt wheelbarrow and cars.

The three men hid their eyes
as love shook off its bars, and earth met paradise.

He left them in the falling snow,
with memories too strange for reckoning,
like his star that rose
and made each one a king.

Susan Skinner

Smiles Like Roses

All down my street
smiles opened like roses
Sun licked me and tickled me
Sun said, *Didn't you believe me*
when I said I'd be back?

I blinked my eyes, I said,
Sun, you are too strong for me
where'd you get those muscles?
Sun said, *Come and dance.*

All over the park
smiles opened like roses
babies kicked off their shoes
and Sun kissed their toes.

All those new babies
all that new sun
everybody dancing
walking but dancing.

All over the world
Sun kicked off his shoes
and came home dancing
licking and tickling,

kissing crossing-ladies and fat babies
saying to everyone,
Hey, you are the most beautiful
dancing people I've ever seen
with those smiles like roses!

Helen Dunmore

Black Dot

a black dot
a jelly tot

a scum-nail
a jiggle-tail

a cool kicker
a sitting slicker

a panting puffer
a fly-snuffer

a high hopper
a belly-flopper

a catalogue
    to make me
        frog.

Libby Houston

Galactic Punctuation

asterisk

a star
astir

a stop
astride

a
space

a spot
as steep

as
space

*

Alexis Lykiard

Mouse

Purposeful

cat

purr (puss full)

Alexis Lykiard

Cat Began

Cat began.
She took the howling of the wind,
She took the screeching of the owl
And made her voice.

For her coat
She took the softness of the snow,
She took the yellow of the sand,
She took the shadows of the branches of the trees.

From deep wells
She took the silences of stones,
She took the moving of the water
For her walk.

Then at night
Cat took the glittering of stars,
She took the blackness of the sky
To make her eyes.

Fire and ice
Went in the sharpness of her claws
And for their shape
She took the new moon's slender curve –

And Cat was made.

Andrew Matthews

Tiger Might

Tiger,
a creature of contrasts.

Here, just demanding to be stroked,
the velvety-soft, striped fur coat.

There, one huge raised paw
that can strike dead gazelle, gnu, or goat.

Tiger,
a creature of contrasts.

Here, the glinting eyes,
pools of shifting light.
        Tiger bright.

There, the watching beast,
tense, lurking in shadows.
        Tiger fear.
        Tiger might.

Wes Magee

The Tyger

Tyger! Tyger! burning bright
In the forests of the night,
What immortal hand or eye
Could frame thy fearful symmetry?

In what distant deeps or skies
Burnt the fire of thine eyes?
On what wings dare he aspire?
What the hand dare seize the fire?

And what shoulder, & what art,
Could twist the sinews of thy heart?
And when thy heart began to beat,
What dread hand? & what dread feet?

What the hammer? what the chain?
In what furnace was thy brain?
What the anvil? what dread grasp
Dare its deadly terrors clasp?

When the stars threw down their spears
And water'd heaven with their tears,
Did he smile his work to see?
Did he who made the Lamb make thee?

William Blake

The Eagle

He clasps the crag with crooked hands;
Close to the sun in lonely lands,
Ringed with the azure world, he stands.

The wrinkled sea beneath him crawls;
He watches from his mountain walls,
And like a thunderbolt he falls.

Alfred Lord Tennyson

Pheasant

Pheasant
strutting like
a lord in a green-
sheen balaclava,
trying to attract a mate,
so he can be a
father,
flicks his
tick of
yellow
eye,
hides
pride behind a
mask, displays his
vicar's collar in this
mixed-up-matching task. He preens red pencilled
feathers, shakes shavings from his back and
points a scaly leg as though he's ready to
attack the dull brown bird he's
spotted but greets her with a
cry that's like a throttled
engine that's threatening
to die.
She
turns away,
this dull brown
bird, plays hard-to-
get which brings a ruffle
to his plumage, a clockwork whir
of wings, a launching of his body,
a tearing of his mind – divided
as his airborne tail as he
leaves her behind.

Gina Douthwaite

A Dog in the Quarry

The day was so bright
    that even birdcages flew open.
The breasts of lawns
    heaved with joy
and the cars on the highway
    sang the great song of asphalt.
At Lobzy a dog fell in the quarry
    and howled.
Mothers pushed their prams out of the park opposite
because babies cannot sleep
    when a dog howls,
and a fat old pensioner was cursing the Municipality:
they let the dog fall in the quarry and then leave him
    there,
and this, if you please, has been going on since morning.

Towards evening even the trees
    stopped blossoming
and the water at the bottom of the quarry
    grew green with death.
But still the dog howled.

Then along came some boys
and made a raft out of two logs
and two planks.
And a man left on the bank
a briefcase . . .
he laid aside his briefcase
and sailed with them.

Their way led across a green puddle
to the island where the dog waited.
It was a voyage like
    the discovery of America,
a voyage like
    the quest of Theseus.
The dog fell silent,
    the boys stood like statues
and one of them punted with a stick,
the waves shimmered nervously,
tadpoles swiftly
    flickered out of the wake,
the heavens
    stood still,
and the man stretched out his hand.

It was a hand
    reaching out across the ages,
it was a hand
    linking
    one world with another,
    life with death,
it was a hand
    joining everything together,
it caught the dog by the scruff of its neck

and then they sailed back
to the music of
an immense fanfare
of the dog's yapping . . .

Miroslav Holub
Czechoslovakian poem translated
by George Theiner

Wolf

Yesterday, in Crawley, I saw a white alsatian
And out of my childhood memories leaped Wolf
The huge white alsatian that terrified me
Every time I walked down Priors Road
Sent by my mum on some errand to the shop.
They say animals can smell your fear;
Wolf seemed to know I was coming
Before I even left our house.
He would lie straddled across the pavement
Like some great battleship,
Or lurk shark-like, in the dark
Passageway between the houses where he lived
Ready to rise up and challenge me
With deep-throated barks that threatened invasion.
I had witnessed his ferocity when he had
Ambushed and demolished other dogs
So I would cross the road to avoid him
Hoping that someone else, or a car,
Would come between us.
Or, when I got to the corner and spied him,
I would turn back to tell my mum
That the shop was closed.

Chris Eddershaw

Horse

The horse at the shore
Casks of red apples, skull, a barrel of rum

The horse in the field
Plough, ploughman, gulls, a furrow, a cornstalk

The horse in the peat-bog
Twelve baskets of dark fire

The horse at the pier
Letters, bread, paraffin, one passenger, papers

The horse at the show
Ribbons, raffia, high bright hooves

The horse in the meadow
A stallion, a red wind, between the hills

The horse at the burn
Quenching a long flame in the throat

George Mackay Brown

Rat It Up

C'mon everybody
Slap some grease on those paws
Get some yellow on your teeth
And, uh, sharpen up your claws

There's a whole lot of sausage
We're gonna swallow down
We're gonna jump out the sewers
And rock this town

Cos we're ratting it up
Yes, we're ratting it up
Well, we're ratting it up
For a ratting good time tonight

Ain't got no compass
You don't need no map
Just follow your snout
Hey, watch out for that trap!

You can take out a poodle
You can beat up a cat
But if you can't lick a ferret
You ain't no kind of rat

Cos we're ratting it up
Yes, we're ratting it up
Well, we're ratting it up
For a ratting good time tonight

Now you can sneak in the henhouse
Roll out the eggs
But if the farmer comes running
Bite his hairy legs

Check the cheese for poison
Before you eat
Or you'll wind up being served up
As ratburger meat

Cos we're ratting it up
Yes, we're ratting it up
Well, we're ratting it up
For a ratting good time tonight

This rat was born to rock
This rat was born to roll
I don't give a monkey's
Bout your pest control

So push off pussy-cat
Push off, pup,
We're the Rockin' Rodents
And we're ratting it up

Yeah, we're ratting it up
Yeah, we're ratting it up
Well, we're ratting it up
For a ratting good time tonight!

Adrian Mitchell

Dazzledance

I have an eye of silver,
I have an eye of gold,
I have a tongue of reed-grass
  and a story to be told.

I have a hand of metal,
I have a hand of clay,
I have two arms of granite
  and a song for every day.

I have a foot of damson,
I have a foot of corn,
I have two legs of leaf-stalk
  and a dance for every morn.

I have a dream of water,
I have a dream of snow,
I have a thought of wildfire
  and a harp-string long and low.

I have an eye of silver,
I have an eye of gold,
I have a tongue of reed-grass
  and a story to be told.

John Rice

Yes

A smile says: Yes.
A heart says: Blood.
When the rain says: Drink
The earth says: Mud.

The kangaroo says: Trampoline.
Giraffes say: Tree.
A bus says: Us
While a car says: Me.

Lemon trees say: Lemons.
A jug says: Lemonade.
The villain says: You're wonderful.
The hero: I'm afraid.

The forest says: Hide and Seek.
The grass says: Green and Grow.
The rail says: Maybe.
The prison says: No.

The millionaire says: Take.
The beggar says: Give.
The soldier cries: Mother!
The baby sings: Live.

The river says: Come with me.
The moon says: Bless.
The stars say: Enjoy the light.
The sun says: Yes.

Adrian Mitchell

The Listeners

'Is there anybody there?' said the Traveller,
Knocking on the moonlit door;
And his horse in the silence champed the grasses
Of the forest's ferny floor;
And a bird flew up out of the turret,
Above the Traveller's head:
And he smote upon the door again a second time;
'Is there anybody there?' he said.
But no one descended to the Traveller;
No head from the leaf-fringed sill
Leaned over and looked into his grey eyes,
Where he stood perplexed and still.
And only a host of phantom listeners
That dwelt in the lone house then
Stood listening in the quiet of the moonlight
To that voice from the world of men:
Stood thronging the faint moonbeams on the dark stair,
That goes down to the empty hall,
Hearkening in an air stirred and shaken
By the lonely Traveller's call.
And he felt in his heart their strangeness,
Their stillness answering his cry,
While his horse moved, cropping the dark turf,
'Neath the starred and leafy sky;
For he suddenly smote on the door, even
Louder, and lifted his head: –
'Tell them I came, and no one answered,
That I kept my word,' he said.
Never the least stir made the listeners,
Though every word he spake

Fell echoing through the shadowiness of the still house
From the one man left awake:
Ay, they heard his foot upon the stirrup,
And the sound of iron on stone,
And how the silence surged softly backward,
When the plunging hoofs were gone.

Walter de la Mare

The Highwayman

The wind a torrent of darkness among the gusty trees,
The moon was a ghostly galleon tossed upon cloudy
seas,
The road was a ribbon of moonlight over the purple
moor,
And the highwayman came riding –
Riding – riding –
The highwayman came riding, up to the old inn-door.

He'd a French cocked-hat on his forehead, a bunch of
lace at his chin,
A coat of claret velvet, and breeches of brown doe-skin;
They fitted with never a wrinkle. His boots were up to
the thigh!
And he rode with a jewelled twinkle,
His pistol butts a-twinkle.
His rapier hilt a-twinkle, under the jewelled sky.

Over the cobbles he clattered and clashed in the dark
inn-yard,
He tapped with his whip on the shutters, but all was
locked and barred;
He whistled a tune to the window, and who should be
waiting there
But the landlord's black-eyed daughter,
Bess, the landlord's daughter,
Plaiting a dark red love-knot into her long black hair.

And in the dark old inn-yard a stable-wicket creaked
Where Tim the ostler listened. His face was white and
 peaked.
His eyes were hollows of madness, his hair like mouldy
 hay,
But he loved the landlord's daughter,
 The landlord's red-lipped daughter.
Dumb as a dog he listened, and he heard the robber
 say –

'One kiss, my bonny sweetheart, I'm after a prize
 tonight,
But I shall be back with the yellow gold before the
 morning light;
Yet, if they press me sharply, and harry me through the
 day,
Then look for me by moonlight,
 Watch for me by moonlight,
I'll come to thee by moonlight, though hell should bar
 the way.'

He rose upright in the stirrups. He scarce could reach
 her hand,
But she loosened her hair i' the casement! His face burnt
 like a brand
As the black cascade of perfume came tumbling over his
 breast;
And he kissed its waves in the moonlight,
 (Oh, sweet black waves in the moonlight!)
Then he tugged at his rein in the moonlight, and
 galloped away to the west.

He did not come in the dawning. He did not come at
noon;
And out o' the tawny sunset, before the rise o' the moon,
A red-coat came marching –
Marching – marching –
King George's men came marching, up to the old inn-
door.

They said no word to the landlord. They drank his ale
instead.
But they gagged his daughter, and bound her, to the foot
of her narrow bed.
Two of them knelt at her casement, with muskets at their
side!
There was death at every window;
And hell at one dark window:
For Bess could see, through her casement, the road that
he would ride.

They had tied her up to attention, with many a
sniggering jest.
They had bound a musket beside her, with the muzzle
beneath her breast!
'Now, keep good watch!' and they kissed her.
She heard the dead man say –
Look for me by moonlight;
Watch for me by moonlight;
I'll come to thee by moonlight, though hell should bar
the way!

She twisted her hands behind her; but all the knots held
good!
She writhed her hands till her fingers were wet with
sweat or blood!
They stretched and strained in the darkness, and the
hours crawled by like years,
Till, now, on the stroke of midnight,
Cold, on the stroke of midnight,
The tip of one finger touched it! The trigger at least was
hers!

The tip of one finger touched it. She strove no more for
the rest.
Up, she stood up to attention, with the muzzle beneath
her breast.
She would not risk their hearing; she would not strive
again;
For the road lay bare in the moonlight;
Bland and bare in the moonlight;
And the blood of her veins, in the moonlight, throbbed
to her love's refrain.

Tlot-tlot; tlot-tlot! Had they heard it? The horse-hoofs
ringing clear;
Tlot-tlot; tlot-tlot, in the distance! Were they deaf that
they did not hear?
Down the ribbon of moonlight, over the brow of the hill,
The highwayman came riding, riding, riding!
The red-coats looked to their priming! She stood up,
straight and still.
Tlot-tlot, in the frosty silence! Tlot-tlot, in the echoing
night!

Nearer he came and nearer. Her face was like a light.
Her eyes grew wide for a moment; she drew one last
deep breath,
Then her finger moved in the moonlight,
Her musket shattered the moonlight,
Shattered her breast in the moonlight and warned him –
with her death.

He turned. He spurred to the west; he did not know who
stood
Bowed, with her head o'er the musket, drenched with
her own red blood!
Not till the dawn he heard it, his face grew grey to hear
How Bess, the landlord's daughter,
The landlord's black-eyed daughter,
Had watched for her love in the moonlight, and died in
the darkness there.

Back, he spurred like a madman, shouting a curse to the
sky,
With the white road smoking behind him and his rapier
brandished high.
Blood-red were his spurs i' the golden noon; wine-red
was his velvet coat;
When they shot him down on the highway,
Down like a dog on the highway,
And he lay in his blood on the highway, with the bunch
of lace at his throat.

And still of a winter's night, they say, when the wind is in
the trees,
When the moon is a ghostly galleon tossed upon a
cloudy seas,
When the road is a ribbon of moonlight over the purple
moor,
A highwayman comes riding –
Riding – riding –
A highwayman comes riding, up to the old inn-door.

Over the cobbles he clatters and clangs in the dark inn-
yard.
And he taps with his whips on the shutters, but all is
locked and barred.
He whistles a tune to the window, and who should be
waiting there
But the landlord's black-eyed daughter,
Bess, the landlord's daughter,
Plaiting a dark red love-knot into her long black hair.

Alfred Noyes

Whose Dem Boots?

Whose dem boots ah hearin, chile,
Whose dem boots ah hear?
Whose dem boots ah hearin, chile,
Whose dem boots ah hear?
Dem boots trampin down de road
Dat fill mah heart wid fear?

Gotta fin' me a hid'n place,
Whai, whai,
Gotta fin' me a hid'n place.

Whose dem boots ah hearin, chile,
Comin thru mah gate?
Whose dem boots ah hearin, chile,
Comin thru mah gate?
Trampin straight up to mah door?
Tell dem please to wait.

Gotta fin' me a hid'n place,
Whai, whai,
Gotta fin' me a hid'n place.

Whose dem boots ah seein, chile,
Stand'n by mah bed?
Whose dem boots ah seein, chile,
Stand'n by mah bed?
Waitin dere so patient, chile?
Tell dem go ahead.

Gotta fin' me a hid'n place,
Whai, whai,
Gotta fin' me a hid'n . . . hunh!

Valerie Bloom

The Sick Rose

O Rose, thou art sick,
The invisible worm
That flies in the night
In the howling storm

Has found out thy bed
Of crimson joy,
And his dark secret love
Does thy life destroy.

William Blake

The Quarrel

I quarrelled with my brother
I don't know what about,
One thing led to another
And somehow we fell out.
The start of it was slight,
The end of it was strong,
He said he was right,
I knew he was wrong!

We hated one another.
The afternoon turned black.
Then suddenly my brother
Thumped me on the back,
And said, 'Oh, *come* along!
We can't go on all night –
I was in the wrong.'
So he was in the right.

Eleanor Farjeon

A Poison Tree

I was angry with my friend:
I told my wrath, my wrath did end.
I was angry with my foe:
I told it not, my wrath did grow.

And I watered it in fears,
Night and morning with my tears;
And I sunned it with smiles,
And with soft deceitful wiles.

And it grew both day and night,
Till it bore an apple bright;
And my foe beheld it shine,
And he knew that it was mine,

And into my garden stole
When the night had veiled the pole:
In the morning glad I see
My foe outstretched beneath the tree.

William Blake

Cross Words

```
                t
    t         w h a m
    r i p       r       d
    i           a   t w i s t           s   s   s c r a p
    p o k e     s   h   g   u         s l a n g   h
        i     s h o u t     g r i p     a   a     u
    b   c l a w     m     c       u   s p i t     c
w r e c k     e     p u l l       n   n     c h o k e
h   a     s h a k e       o   s   c   a     h
a   t     n   r         h u r l   h u r t
c     s   e     s t a b   t   i       l
k     w r e n c h     i       n   j
      a   r     o     f   s   g r a b
      t     r a v e   f l o g     b a n g
    b       a   e         c         t
    a       n     k n o c k     h i t
    s c r a t c h       u           l e t ' s
    h                   f         b e
                        f         e
                                  s
                              m a t e s
```

Gina Douthwaite

You're

Clownlike, happiest on your hands,
Feet to the stars, and moon-skulled,
Gilled like a fish. A common-sense
Thumbs down on the dodo's mode.
Wrapped up in yourself like a spool,
Trawling your dark as owls do,
Mute as a turnip from the Fourth
Of July to All Fool's Day,
O high-riser, my little loaf.

Vague as fog and looked for like mail,
Farther off than Australia.
Bent-backed Atlas, our travelled prawn.
Snug as bud and at home
Like a sprat in a pickle jug.
A creel of eels, all ripples.
Jumpy as a Mexican bean.
Right, like a well-done sum.
A clean slate, with your own face on.

Sylvia Plath

High Dive

It feels very lonely, up here against the clouds
and girders of the glass roof. The pool so far away,
framed in flowers of a thousand upturned faces.

Walk to the brink, turn, and carefully
(firm toes gripping this last hold on life)
hang heels in space. Face a blank wall.

Raise arms slowly, sideways, shoulder-high,
silent passion, dream-deep concentration
foretelling every second of the coming flight.

Then with a sudden upward beat of palms,
of arms like wings, gathering more than thought
launch backwards into take-off, into one ball

roll for a quadruple reverse somersault
that at the last split second flicks
open like a switchblade –

feet pointed as in prayer, neat-folded hands
stab the heavens like a dagger, plunge
deep into the pool's azure flesh – without a splash.

James Kirkup

Growler

Like a toad
beneath a suddenly
flipped stone

huffed up
as if about
to sing (but no

sound comes)
yes, it was me.
I was the one

who cracked the bell
of everyone's *Hey-*
Ring-A-Ding-Ding-

Sweet-Lovers-Love-the . . .
'Stop!' Miss Carver
clapped her hands.

'Which one of you's
the Growler?' No one
breathed. 'Very well.

Sing on.' And she leaned
very close
all down the line till

'Stop!'
She was as small as me
(aged eight)

but sour and sixty,
savage for the love
of her sweet music

I was curdling.
'You!
How *dare* you?

Out!' Down the echoing
hall, all eyes on me . . .
My one big solo.

She died last year.
I hope somebody sang.
Me, I'm still growling.

Philip Gross

West Indian Bouncers

The brother
Who taught me cricket
With a nice soft tennis ball
On the lawn
Is today toughening me up,
Giving me the 'treatment' –
West Indian style –
With a hard rubber ball
On the sun-baked, bumpy,
Dust bowl behind the dog shed.
I duck and dodge as
A barrage of bouncers
Savagely rear up at me
Chin height
From just short of a length
To crash against the shed
Behind my head.
The dogs bark furiously
And Mum yells at us from the kitchen
To stop!
But the bombardment continues –
There are still two overs to survive
Before lunch.

Chris Eddershaw

Oath of Friendship

SHANG YA!
I want to be your friend
For ever and ever without break or decay.
When the hills are all flat
And the rivers are all dry,
When it lightens and thunders in winter,
When it rains and snows in summer,
When Heaven and Earth mingle –
Not till then will I part from you.

Author Unknown
(First century BC)
translated by Arthur Waley

Night Puzzle

can I sleep with those words going round and round my head and why did you say those words you said and how

Roger Stevens

Don't Be Scared

The dark is only a blanket
for the moon to put on her bed.

The dark is a private cinema
for the movie dreams in your head.

The dark is a little black dress
to show off the sequin stars.

The dark is the wooden hole
behind the strings of happy guitars.

The dark is a jeweller's velvet cloth
where children sleep like pearls.

The dark is a spool of film
to photograph boys and girls,

so smile in your sleep in the dark.
Don't be scared.

Carol Ann Duffy

Nettles

My son aged three fell in the nettle bed.
'Bed' seemed a curious name for those green spears,
That regiment of spite behind the shed:
It was no place for rest. With sobs and tears
The boy came seeking comfort and I saw
White blisters beaded on his tender skin.
We soothed him till his pain was not so raw.
At last he offered us a watery grin,
And then I took my billhook, honed the blade
And went outside and slashed in fury with it
Till not a nettle in that fierce parade
Stood upright any more. And then I lit
A funeral pyre to burn the fallen dead,
But in two weeks the busy sun and rain
Had called up tall recruits behind the shed:
My son would often feel sharp wounds again.

Vernon Scannell

Thistles

Against the rubber tongues of cows and the hoeing
hands of men
Thistles spike the summer air
Or crackle open under a blue-black pressure.

Every one a revengeful burst
Of resurrection, a grasped fistful
Of splintered weapons and Icelandic frost thrust up

From the underground stain of a decayed Viking.
They are like pale hair and the gutturals of dialects.
Every one manages a plume of blood.

Then they grow grey, like men.
Mown down, it is a feud. Their sons appear,
Stiff with weapons, fighting back over the same ground.

Ted Hughes

The 1st

What I remember about that day
is boxes stacked across the walk
and couch springs curling through the air
and drawers and tables balanced on the kerb
and us, hollering,
leaping up and around
happy to have a playground;

nothing about the emptied rooms
nothing about the emptied family

Lucille Clifton

Listening to grownups quarrelling

standing in the hall against the
wall with my little brother, blown
like leaves against the wall by their
voices, my head like a pingpong ball
between the paddles of their anger:
I knew what it meant
to tremble like a leaf.

Cold with their wrath, I heard
the claws of the rain
pounce. Floods
poured through the city,
skies clapped over me,
and I was shaken, shaken
like a mouse
between their jaws.

Ruth Whitman

Hammer

The best football player our school ever had
Was Mohammed Abdallah, or Hammer, for short,
'Cause he hammered the ball like a shot from a gun.
He was clever but modest, funny and fun,
Wicked at maths and fantastic at sport.

He jumped like a cat,
Sprinted like lightning,
Dodged in and out
So fast it was frightening!

The best football player our school ever had
Taught us all about where he grew up – Pakistan.
He opened our minds to that marvellous place,
And shared his dream with us (a smile on his face);
To fly back and visit his grandad and gran.

He warmed the whole class
With his special charm.
If only we'd known
Someone else meant him harm.

The best football player our school ever had
Was chosen by two boys from class 7A.
They followed him slyly, when no one was near,
Whispering threats, that filled him with fear,
Mocking his name as he hurried away.

They mumbled their plans,
The time and the date,
With cold, eager fists
And eyes full of hate.

The best football player our school ever had
Decided to try for a part in a play.
He waited behind, one wet afternoon,
And at the audition, he sang every tune,
Acted with style, then went on his way.

But stepping outside,
He was met by four eyes,
In two vicious faces;
The 7A guys!

The best football player our school ever had,
Felt one grabbing hand at the back of his head,
But quick as a rocket, he twisted and tugged.
He had to escape, escape or be mugged!
With insults and shouts in his ears, off he sped.

His heart beat as fast
As his feet on the yard,
His lungs gasping air
And his pulse pounding hard.

The best football player our school ever had
Dashed out through the gates and into the street.
The 7A thugs soon gave up the chase,
He looked back as he ran, with relief on his face,
Shot into the road and was knocked off his feet.

With wide sorry eyes
The thugs called his name,
Awaiting an answer.

None ever came.

Darren Stanley

Bullies

With the eye in the back of his head
he sees them coming –

eight-year-old breakers,
baby-hard, baby-soft.

Their space-machine, so elegant
could swallow him,

drown him once and for all
in a dish of air.

No use trying to rewrite the law:
they are the masters –

skills bred in the bone.
He freezes –

they expect it,
though a voice inside him squeaks

I . . . Words cut his tongue
weigh in his mind like a bruise.

Katherine Gallagher

The Hate

We began each morning with hymns,
'Lots of wind,' our teacher called
as she wrestled a melody
from the ancient hall piano.

Then we sat and gazed at the front
while the football results were read
and Donald was led in, held by the arm,
a look of alarm on his face.
I didn't know what he'd done,
perhaps he'd stolen or two-fingered
once too often. It must have been serious
in the eyes of God, in the eyes
of our headmistress.

She seemed to think
that boys' backsides were meant to be whacked,
but Donald struggled and lay on the floor
and flapped like a fish out of water.
Even the toughies were terrified
as the slipper rose and fell
a total of eighteen times till it stopped
and Donald stayed locked to the floor.

The piano was open but no one played
as we filed out silent and found our maths.
It stayed on our minds for much of the day
but Donald wouldn't say what he'd done
just shook his head and said nothing.

Our teacher said Donald would be forgiven,
start once again and clean the slate;
but I glimpsed him next day in prayers,
a dreadful look on his face, and I knew
it would take more than Jesus
to wipe away the hate.

Brian Moses

Knot True

I never lie!
Would I deny I do, if it were true? If ever I did lie then I deny it. Yes! I do.
I do, I don't tell lies, I won't tell lies if I untie the knots I've not got tangled in because I never lie!

Gina Douthwaite

A Boy's Head

In it there is a space-ship
and a project
for doing away with piano lessons.

And there is
Noah's ark,
which shall be first.

And there is
an entirely new bird,
an entirely new hare,
an entirely new bumble-bee.

There is a river
that flows upwards.

There is a multiplication table.

There is anti-matter.

And it just cannot be trimmed.

I believe
that only what cannot be trimmed
is a head.

There is much promise
in the circumstance
that so many people have heads.

Miroslav Holub
Czechoslovakian poem
translated by Ian Milner

A Girl's Head

(*after the poem, 'A Boy's Head' by Miroslav Holub*)

In it there is a dream
that was started
before she was born,

and there is a globe
with hemispheres
which shall be happy.

There is her own spacecraft,
a chosen dress
and pictures of her friends.

There are shining rings
and a maze of mirrors.

There is a diary
for surprise occasions.

There is a horse springing hooves
across the sky.

There is a sea that
tides and swells
and cannot be mapped.

There is untold hope
in that no equation exactly
fits a head.

Katherine Gallagher

Rupa's Hand

Can you sketch?
Rupa can.
A house, a horse, a mouse, a man.

Her hand is the pencil bird,
Watch it fly,
Looping the loop
Through the sketchbook sky.

Can you paint?
Rupa's the best.
A fish, a fire, a treasure chest.

Her hand is the brush dancer,
Watch it wind
Through a pencilled maze,
Leaving trails behind.

Can you draw?
Rupa's great.
A chair, a child, a garden gate.

Her hand is the pastel shark,
Watch it slash
Through coloured seas
With a rainbow splash.

Can you shade?
Rupa does.
A smudge, a smear, a feathered fuzz.

Her hand is the charcoal flower,
Watch it grow,
Shedding fine, grey seeds
On white fields below.

Can you hear
Rupa's heart?
Its beat is captured in her art.

Darren Stanley

Warning

When I am an old woman I shall wear purple
With a red hat which doesn't suit me,
And I shall spend my pension on brandy and summer
gloves
And satin sandals, and say we've no money for butter.
I shall sit down on the pavement when I'm tired
And gobble up samples in shops and press alarm bells
And run my stick along the public railings
And make up for the sobriety of my youth.
I shall go out in my slippers in the rain
And pick the flowers in other people's gardens
And learn to spit.

You can wear terrible shirts and grow more fat
And eat three pounds of sausages at a go
Or only bread and pickle for a week
And hoard pens and pencils and beermats and things in
boxes.

But now we must have clothes that keep us dry
And pay the rent and not swear in the street
And set a good example for the children.
We must have friends to dinner and read the papers.

But maybe I ought to practise a little now?
So people who know me are not too shocked and
surprised
When suddenly I am old and start to wear purple.

Jenny Joseph

She

She is air and light –
Sun and moon and stars and loosened flame;
We are shadows dancing in her name.
She's quicksilver, a vein of gold
In ordinary day,
The play
Of leaves and ripples charged with energy.
She's wind and fire and darkness and desire,
Cymbal-clash and brush of thistledown,
Lightning-flash
Across the brain, a spark struck out between
Cold iron and cold stone,
A sudden rainbow in a drop of rain.

Phoebe Hesketh

She is

She is like a golden star,
slinking into the night.
She is like a flower of light.
She is like a silent pair of lips
saying something uknown.
She is like a brilliant spurt of love.
She is like an ungrateful silence.

Matthew Cole

Swineherd

'When all this is over,' said the swineherd,
'I mean to retire, where
Nobody will have heard about my special skills
And conversation is mainly about the weather.

I intend to learn how to make coffee, at least as well
As the Portuguese lay-sister in the kitchen
And polish the brass fenders every day.
I want to lie awake at night
Listening to cream crawling to the top of the jug.
And the water lying soft in the cistern.

I want to see an orchard where the trees grow in straight
 lines
And the yellow fox finds shelter between the navy-blue
 trunks,
Where it gets dark early in summer
And the apple-blossom is allowed to wither on the
 bough.'

Eiléan Ní Chuilleanáin

Under a Ramshackle Rainbow

A dead tree.
On a rotten branch sit two wingless birds. Among leaves
on the ground a man is searching for his hands.
It is fall.

A stagnant marsh.
On a mossy stone sits the man angling. The hook
is stuck in the waterlily.
The waterlily is stuck in the mud.

An overgrown ruin.
In the grass the man sleeps sitting up. A raindrop
descends
in slow-motion through space.
Somewhere in the grass a pike flounders.

A dry well.
At the bottom lies a dead fly. In the wood nearby
a spider gropes through the fog.
The man is trapped in the spiderweb on the horizon.

An abandoned ant hill.
Above a little woodmarsh floats the man. The sun
is just going down. The man has already stopped
growing.
The ants gather on the shore.

Ingemar Gustafson
translated from the Swedish by May Swenson

Maze

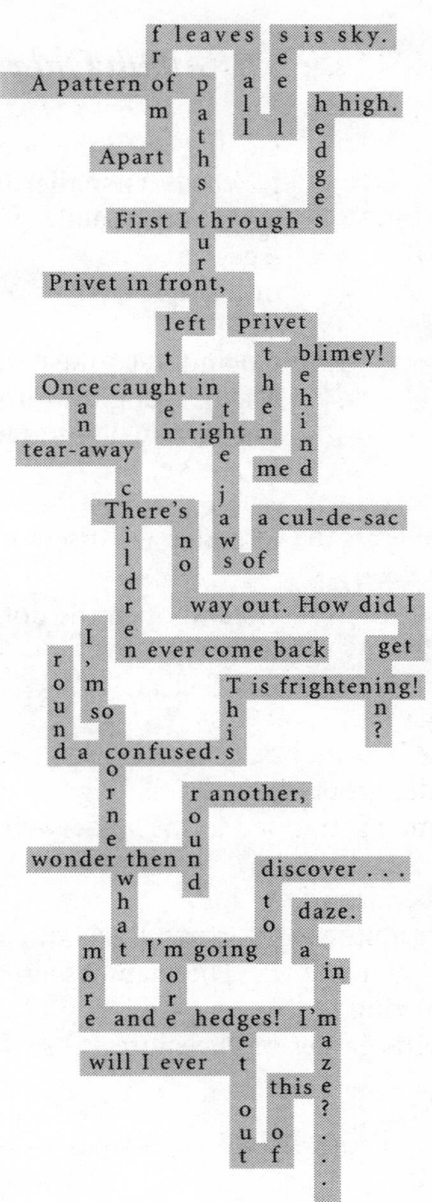

Gina Douthwaite

The Door

Go and open the door.
Maybe outside there's
a tree, or a wood,
a garden,
or a magic city.

Go and open the door.
Maybe a dog's rummaging.
Maybe you'll see a face,
or an eye,
or the picture
of a picture.

Go and open the door.
If there's a fog
it will clear.

Go and open the door.
Even if there's only
the darkness ticking,
even if there's only
the hollow wind,
even if
nothing
is there,
go and open the door.

At least
there'll be
a draught.

Miroslav Holub

Wings

If I had wings
I would touch the fingertips of clouds
and glide on the wind.

If I had wings
I would taste a chunk of the sun
as hot as peppered curry.

If I had wings
I would listen to the clouds of sheep bleat
that graze on the blue.

If I had wings
I would breathe deep and sniff
the scent of raindrops.

If I had wings
I would gaze at the people
who cling to the earth.

If I had wings
I would dream of
walking the deserts
and swimming the seas.

Pie Corbett

Southbound on the Freeway

A tourist came in from Orbitville,
parked in the air, and said:

The creatures of this star
are made of metal and glass.

Through the transparent parts
you can see their guts.

Their feet are round and roll
on diagrams – or long

measuring tapes – dark
with white lines.

They have four eyes.
The two in the back are red.

Sometimes you can see a 5-eyed
one, with a red eye turning

on the top of his head.
He must be special –

the others respect him,
and go slow,

when he passes, winding
among them from behind.

They all hiss as they glide,
like inches, down the marked

tapes. Those soft shapes,
shadowy inside

the hard bodies – are they
their guts or their brains?

May Swenson

The Refrigerator's Belly

Always something going on in there,
little gurglings and slurps, and we feed it
all we have: butter, eggs, cheese, cold meats,
desserts in packets, tomatoes, spring onions,
left-overs, salads, ice-cubes, milk bottles.

What an investment. Its cold mouth shuts.
There's no throat, no gullet, all goes straight down
into the ice bucket of the belly, like Jonah or Gepetto,
the slow digestion working with sighs of resignation
and the waiting, waiting, waiting,

all that frozen wisdom, the opening of the door,
the world having ticked on with its comings and
goings
and constant decaying.
Put your ear to the door. You can hear the meat
        thinking.
You can hear the cheese muttering.

Life inside the belly. Life inside the whale.

George Szirtes

Comida / Food

Uno se come
la luna en la tortilla
comes frijol
y comes tierra
Comes chile
y comes sol y feugo
Bebes agua
y bebes cielo

One eats
the moon in a tortilla
Eat frijoles
and you eat the earth
Eat chile
and you eat sun and fire
Drink water
and you drink sky

Victor M. Valle

Glitterbread

I'm so bored with pitta bread
I want glitterbread.
Bread that gleams when it catches the light,
Bread that glows like the stars at night,
Bread that sparkles then starts to shimmer,
Bread that dazzles and never grows dimmer,
Bread that lights my way back home,
Bread that shines like a precious stone.
I want glitterbread all the time,
Something new that's totally mine.

Brian Moses

The Magic Box

I will put in the box

the swish of a silk sari on a summer night,
fire from the nostrils of a Chinese dragon,
the tip of a tongue touching a tooth.

I will put in the box

a snowman with a rumbling belly,
a sip of the bluest water from Lake Lucerne,
a leaping spark from an electric fish.

I will put in the box

three violet wishes spoken in Gujarati,
the last joke of an ancient uncle
and the first smile of a baby.

I will put in the box

a fifth season and a black sun,
a cowboy on a broomstick
and a witch on a white horse.

My box is fashioned from ice and gold and steel,
with stars on the lid and secrets in the corners.
Its hinges are the toe joints
of dinosaurs.

I shall surf in my box
on the great high-rolling breakers of the wild Atlantic,
then wash ashore on a yellow beach
the colour of the sun.

Kit Wright

Getting Rid of the Box

The box had five locks
and four false floors,
and a welded-shut door.

And six men carried it
to a nuclear submarine
which burrowed through the ocean

to the first icy suburb
of Antarctica, where no
human marked the ice or snow.

The captain gave the order
to unleash a torpedo
as deep in the ice as it would go,

then in the blast hole
he offloaded the box
and covered it with ice-rocks,

then a second torpedo
brought more ice collapsing
onto the nauseous thing,

and at last he knew
the box's grisly cargo
was as safe as the snow,

and none of that stuff
we all crammed in
would ever bother us again.

Matthew Sweeney

Fairy Tale

He built himself a house,
    his foundations,
    his stones,
    his walls,
    his roof overhead,
    his chimney and smoke,
    his view from the window.

He made himself a garden,
    his fence,
    his thyme,
    his earthworm,
    his evening dew.

He cut out his bit of sky above.

And he wrapped the garden in the sky
and the house in the garden
and packed the lot in a handkerchief

and went off
lone as an arctic fox
through the cold
unending
rain
into the world.

Miroslav Holub
Translated by Ian Milner and George Theiner

What Would You Do if the Moon?

What would you do if the moon
were a butterfly in its cocoon?
Order the airforce to guard the cabbages.

What would you do if the moon
grew bright leaves and petals next June?
Pluck it and put it the hair of the milky way.

What would you do if the moon
let down its wheels and went off with a zoom?
Hitch-hike a lift to the nearest galaxy.

What would you do if the moon
were to burst in a shower with a boom?
Make a million pieces of cheese on toast.

What would you do if the moon
dropped down to earth like a prune?
Buy up the complete stocks of custard powder.

What would you do if the moon
went blue and became a balloon?
Invite the whole world to a special party.

What would you do if the moon
started turning and playing a tune?
Ask all the guests to start dancing.

What would you do if the moon
unwound its ribbon into a festoon?
Cut it up and throw it over the dancers.

What would you do if the moon
shouted, 'Save me. Please save me soon?'
Tell the presidents to make peace at once.

What would you do if the moon
gave up the ghost on a grey afternoon?
I don't know. What do you suggest?

Dennis Carter

The Magical Mouse

I am the magical mouse
I don't eat cheese
I eat sunsets
And the tops of trees

I don't wear fur

I wear funnels
Of lost ships and the weather
That's under dead leaves
I am the magical mouse

I don't fear cats

Or woodsowls
I do as I please
Always
I don't eat crusts
I am the magical mouse
I eat
Little birds – and maidens

That taste like dust

Kenneth Patchen

Kubla Khan

In Xanadu did Khubla Khan
A stately pleasure-dome decree:
Where Alph, the sacred river, ran
Through caverns measureless to man
Down to a sunless sea.
So twice five miles of fertile ground
With walls and towers were girdled round:
And there were gardens bright with sinuous rills,
Where blossomed many an incense-bearing tree;
And here were forests ancient as the hills,
Enfolding sunny spots of greenery.

But oh! that deep romantic cavern which slanted
Down the green hill athwart a cedarn cover!
A savage place! as holy and enchanted
As e'er beneath a waning moon was haunted
By woman wailing for her demon lover!
And from this cavern, with ceaseless turmoil seething,
As if this earth in fast, thick pants were breathing,
A mighty fountain momently was forced:
Amid whose swift half-intermitted burst
Huge fragments vaulted like rebounding hail,
Or chaffy grain beneath the thresher's flail:
And 'mid these dancing rocks at once and ever
It flung up momently the sacred river.

Five miles meandering with a mazy motion
Through wood and dale the sacred river ran,
Then reached the caverns measureless to man,
And sank in tumult to a lifeless ocean:

And 'mid this tumult Kubla heard from far
Ancestral voices prophesying war!

The shadow of the dome of pleasure
Floated midway on the waves;
Where was heard the mingled measure
From the fountain and the caves.
It was a miracle of rare device,
A sunny pleasure-dome with caves of ice!

A damsel with a dulcimer
In a vision once I saw:
It was an Abyssinian maid,
And on her dulcimer she played,
Singing of Mount Arbora.
Could I revive within me
Her symphony and song,
To such a deep delight 'twould win me,
That with music loud and long,
I would build a dome in air.
That sunny dome! those caves of ice!
And all who heard should see them there,
And all should cry, Beware! Beware!
His flashing eyes, his floating hair!
Weave a circle round him thrice,
And close your eyes with holy dread,
For he on honey-dew hath fed,
And drunk the milk of Paradise.

Samuel Taylor Coleridge

Thief

From *Six Go Through the World*

Small things are easy; flowers, what was said,
colour from your hair. Others
need practise. Heat of summers.
The certainty things ever really happened.

While you sleep I rifle whole years,
stories you think you know, names and faces.
Legends behind constellations.
The way back home. Old fears.

You won't see them go, a pause at a railway crossing,
A footpath, what lies beyond the forest.
Smooth skin on your forehead. Breath to run.
Take a look. Most of yesterday is missing.

I admit my limits. Can't undo
that combination lock you keep on your desire
to make words rhyme. The craze for trees.
Barrows in the corners of fields defy me

though my accomplices, wind and rain
plunder them all night.
Deep in cathedrals I burgle the dust of saints
on TV make daylight robbery of reputations.

I leer out from women's mirrors,
in libraries fray pages from old books.
Who'll even know the stories are going,
the poems being whittled away?

My one fear is some shadow I might snatch
will be my own. There's too much
world without me. Who'll take
your nightmares then, the fierce despairs

of children, terror of the future? And when
the quest is over who'll be merciful?
Who'll relieve you of your
hunger to go on?

Catherine Fisher

Words

come out
like stars sometimes
and choose the darkest nights
to sparkle in,

are gentle
water-drops suggesting
streams you cannot find the source of
in a landscape where no
water is,

or wasps
behind your back which
suddenly
go silent.

John Mole

A Word is Dead

A word is dead
When it is said,
Some say.
I say it just
Begins to live
That day.

Emily Dickinson

Acknowledgements

The publishers wish to thank the following for permission to use copyright materials:

John Agard: 'Secret' from *Another Day on Your Foot*, by permission of Caroline Sheldon Literary Agency on behalf of the author. **James Berry:** 'Benediction' from *Chain Of Days*, (Oxford University Press), by permission of the Peters Fraser and Dunlop Group Ltd on behalf of the author. **Valerie Bloom:** 'Whose Dem Boots?', from *The World is Sweet*, Bloomsbury Children's Books, 2000, by permission of the author. **Dennis Carter:** 'What Would You Do if the Moon?', from *Sleeplessness Jungle*, Clwyd Poetry project, Mold (Pentre Farm, Woodhill, Oswestry, Shropshire). **Eiléan Ní Chuilleanáin:** 'Swinherd', from *The Second Voyage*, Gallery Press 1977; **Lucille Clifton**: 'The 1st', copyright © 1987 Lucille Clifton. Reprinted from *Good Woman: Poems and a Memoir 1969-1980*, BOA Editions, Ltd. 260 East Avenue, Rochester, NY 14604. **John Coldwell:** 'Beach', by permission of the author. **Matthew Cole:** 'She is', first published in *Catapults and Kingfishers*, edited by Pie Corbett and Brian Moses, 1986, Oxford University Press. **David Constantine:** 'Coltsfoot', from *Madder*, Bloodaxe, 1987. **Pie Corbett**, 'A poem to be spoken silently . . .', 'Sunday Morning Diary Poem', 'Wings', by permission of the author. **Teddy Corbett**: 'Clouds', from *Inky Foot*, Macmillan, (1998), by permission of the author. **Sue Cowling**: 'Winter Morning', by permission of the author. **Gina Douthwaite**: 'Sunset', 'Pheasant', 'Knot True', by permission of the author, © Gina Douthwaite 2001; 'Cross Words', 'Maze', first published in *Picture a Poem*, Hutchinson, 1994, by permission of the author. **Carol Ann Duffy**: 'Don't be scared', from *The Oldest Girl in the World*, 'Three' from *The Oldest Girl in the World*, (2001) by permission of Faber and Faber Ltd. **Helen Dunmore**: 'Smiles like roses', by permission of Scholastic Ltd, from *Snollygoster* © Helen Dunmore 2001. **Chris Eddershaw**: 'Wolf', 'West Indian Bouncers', by permission of the author. **Eleanor Farjeon**: 'The Quarrel', copyright Gervase Farjeon. **Catherine Fisher**: 'Thief', from *Six go through the world.* **Katherine Gallagher**: 'Bullies', first published in *Them and Us*, Bodley Head 1993, by permission of the author; 'A Girl's Head', from *Fish-rings on Water*, Forest Books, 1989, by permission of the author. **Philip Gross**: 'Growler', from *The All-Nite Café*, Faber 1993, by permission of Faber and Faber Ltd. **Phoebe Hesketh**: 'Heatwave', 'She', *From A Song Of Sunlight*, Chatto and Windus, 1974. **Libby Houston**: 'Black Dot', from *All Change*, Oxford University Press, 1993. **Miroslav Holub**: 'A Boy's Head', 'The Door', 'Fairy tale', from *Poems before and After*, Bloodaxe Books, 1990, © translation by Ian Milner and George Thiener. 'A dog in the Quarry', translation copyright © 1967 Penguin Books, from *Miroslav Holub: Selected Poems* translated by Ian Milner (Penguin, 1967). **Ted Hughes**: 'Thistles', from Wodwo 1967, Faber and Faber Ltd. **Jenny Joseph**: 'Warning', from *Selected Poems*, Bloodaxe Books Ltd. Copyright Jenny Joseph 1992, by permission of John Johnson (Literary Agent) Ltd on behalf of the author. **James Kirkup**: for 'High Dive'. **Karla Kuskin**: for 'Where would you be?' **Frank O'Hara**: 'Les Etiquettes jaune', from *The Collected Poems of Frank O'Hara*, Grove Press 1974; **Amy Lowell**: 'Wind and Silver', from *The Complete Poetical Works of Amy Lowell*, copyright

1955 by Houhgton Mifflin Co, © renewed 1983 by Houghton Mifflin Co, Brinton P.Roberts and G. D'Andelot Belin, Esq. Previously published in What's O'Clock. All rights reserved. **Alexis Lykiard**: 'Galactic Punctuation', 'Mouse', from *Selected Poems 1956-1996*, 1996, Salzburg University. **George Mackay Brown**: 'Horse', from *Selected Poems 1954-1992*, 1991, John Murray. **Wes Magee**: 'Tiger Might', by permission of the author. **Walter de la Mare**: 'The Listeners', from *The Complete Poems of Walter de La Mare*, 1969, by permission of the Literary trustees of the author and The Society of Authors as their representative. **Andrew Matthews**: 'Cat Began', from *Paws and Claws*, Hutchinson Children's Books, 1995. **Adrian Mitchell**: 'Rat it up', 'Yes', reprinted by permission of PFD on behalf of: Adrian Mitchell. © Adrian Mitchell: as printed in the original volume. Adrian Mitchell's work is not be used in any examination whatsoever. **John Mole**: 'Words', from *Hot Air* (Hodder 1996), by permission of the author. **Brian Moses**: 'The Hate', 'Glitterbread', from *Barking Back at Dogs*, Macmillan Children's Books 2000, by permission of the author. **Alfred Noyes**: 'The Highwayman' from *Collected Poems*, by permission of John Murray Publishers Ltd. **Emanuel diPasquale**: 'Rain', copyright © 1999 by Emanuel diPasquale. Used by Marian Reiner for the author. **Kenneth Patchen**: 'The Magical Mouse', from *The Collected Poems of Kenneth Patchen*, © 1952 by Kenneth Patchen. New Directions Publishing Corp. **Sylvia Plath**: 'You're', from *Collected Poems* by Sylvia Plath, by permission of Faber and Faber Ltd. **Vasko Popa**: 'Winter' and 'Snow', from *The Golden Apple*, translated Andrew Harvey and Anne Pennington, London: Anvil, 1980. **James Reeves**: 'The Sea', from *Complete Poems for Children*, Heinemann. © James Reeves, by permission of Laura Cecil Literary Agency on behalf of the estate of the author. **John Rice**: 'This morning I have risen early', 'Atlantic Roundhouse', from *The Dream of Night Fishers*, Scottish Cultural Press 1998, by permission of the author; 'Dazzledance', from *An Odd Kettle of Fish*, Macmillan 1995 by permission of the author. **Carl Sandburg**: 'Fog', Copyright © 1944 Carl Sandburg from *Chicago Poems* by Carl Sandburg (Harcourt Brace, 1944); 'Splinter', copyright 1928 and renewed 1956 by Carl Sandburg. Harcourt Brace and Co. **Vernon Scannell**: 'Nettles', by permission of the author. **Susan Skinner**: for 'Three Kings'. **Darren Stanley**: 'Hammer', 'Rupa's Hand', by permission of the author. **Roger Stevens**: 'Night Puzzle', by permission of the author. **Matthew Sweeney**: 'Getting Rid of the Box', from *Up on the Roof*, Selected Poems by permission of Faber and Faber Ltd. **May Swenson**: translation of 'Under a Ramshackle Rainbow', from *Exploring Poetry*, ed. Geoff Fox and Dennis Pepper, 1991, NATE. 'Southbound on the Freeway', from *To Mix with Time*, By May Swenson, to Charles Scribner's Sons. **George Szirtes**: 'The Refrigerator's Belly', by permission of the author. **Victor M. Valle**: 'Comida/Food', from *Fiesta in Aztlan*, Capra Press. **Ruth Whitman**: 'Listening to grown ups quarreling', copyright © 1968 and renewed 1996 by Ruth Whitman. Harcourt Brace and Co. Lari Williams, 'Before the hunt', from *You'll Love This Stuff*, ed. Morag styles, 1986, Cambridge University Press. Kit Wright, 'The Magic Box', from *Cat Among the Pigeons*, Viking Kestrel 1987.

Every effort has been made to trace the copyright holders but if any have been inadvertently overlooked the publishers will be pleased to make the necessary arrangement at the first opportunity.